Crocodile Ride

Crocodile said to his wife one night,
"Will you come with me in this bright moonlight
on our brand-new bikes for a nine-mile ride?"
"All right," said his bride, but she turned and sighed

2

"At this t<u>ime</u> of n<u>igh</u>t, a r<u>ide</u> on a b<u>ike</u>
isn't qu<u>ite</u> what <u>I</u> would really l<u>ike</u>."

Croc just smil_e_d and said, "Let's try.

You'll f_i_nd these b_i_k_e_s can really fly!"

4

Off down the hill they began to gli_de_.

"You see," said Croc, "it's a very fi_ne_ ri_de_.

Be glad that you took my adv_ice_.

A h_ike_ on a b_ike_ is really n_ice_."

His wife replied, "Take my advice,
or you may have to pay the price.
Put your glasses on, if you don't mind.
Without them you are almost blind!"

Too late! Croc got an awful fri<u>ght</u>.

At the bottom of the hill, he didn't turn r<u>ight</u>!

Newt's Flute

In the light of the m<u>oo</u>n, one night in J<u>u</u>n<u>e</u>,

N<u>ew</u>t got out a fl<u>u</u>t<u>e</u> and bl<u>ew</u> out a t<u>u</u>n<u>e</u>.

Shrew said, "It's late, and I'm not in the mood.

To play a tune at night is really quite rude!

I was trying to snooze. Now I'm starting to fume!"

And he jumped up and scooted out of his room.

"Listen, N<u>ew</u>t!" he said. "I don't wish t<u>o</u> arg<u>ue</u>,
but there's something I think it's time that <u>you</u> kn<u>ew</u>.
N<u>ew</u>ts that play the fl<u>u</u>t<u>e</u> well are tr<u>u</u>ly quite f<u>ew</u>,
and those n<u>ew</u>ts really d<u>o</u> not incl<u>u</u>d<u>e</u> <u>you</u>!"

Shrew's
House

12

Newt began to fume, and he said, "That isn't fair!
But to tell you the truth, I really do not care!"
And he blew on his flute and played a new tune.
Shrew zoomed off, saying, "I'll be back very soon."

He fetched a huge tube, and he blew "toot, toot!"
"I can be as rude as you," he said to Newt.

Then Owl swooped down and said, "What I will do, is to take that flute and that tube from you."

And so, very s<u>oo</u>n, there was no more t<u>u</u>n<u>e</u>,
and Owl could sn<u>oo</u>ze in the light of the m<u>oo</u>n.

Snake's Cake

Snail made up his mind that he would make a birthday cake for his best mate, Snake. But Snail, I'm afraid, was a little bit lazy and, some would say, a little bit crazy!

He m<u>a</u>de up <u>a</u> tr<u>ay</u> with <u>a</u> cup and <u>a</u> pl<u>ate</u>.

"I <u>ai</u>m to surprise Sn<u>ake</u>—I really can't w<u>ai</u>t!

I'll give this c<u>ake</u> an am<u>a</u>zing t<u>aste</u>.

Let's t<u>ake</u> <u>a</u> look here—there's no time to w<u>aste</u>."

"That's a pain," he said, as he came to the page.

"If I make it like that, it will take me an age.

I'll have to race to the store if I do what they say.

I'll just make this cake in my own special way."

So in went some d<u>a</u>t<u>e</u>s and some st<u>a</u>l<u>e</u> cornfl<u>a</u>k<u>e</u>s.

Then Sn<u>ai</u>l g<u>a</u>v<u>e</u> the mix <u>a</u> few really good sh<u>a</u>k<u>e</u>s.

"I'll put in some gr<u>a</u>p<u>e</u>s, if there's any sp<u>a</u>c<u>e</u>,"

said that cr<u>a</u>zy Sn<u>ai</u>l, with <u>a</u> smile on his f<u>a</u>c<u>e</u>.

When Sn<u>a</u>k<u>e</u> c<u>a</u>m<u>e</u>, Sn<u>ai</u>l pl<u>a</u>c<u>e</u>d the tr<u>ay</u> on the tabl

"Eat the whole c<u>a</u>k<u>e</u>, m<u>a</u>t<u>e</u>," said Sn<u>ai</u>l, "if you're ab

I m<u>a</u>d<u>e</u> it to wish you <u>a</u> 'Happy Birthd<u>ay</u>.'

I'm sure it will t<u>a</u>st<u>e</u> good. What do you s<u>ay</u>?"

"I'm wondering why you m<u>a</u>d<u>e</u> this c<u>a</u>k<u>e</u> tod<u>ay</u>.

It isn't my birthd<u>ay</u> until Saturd<u>ay</u>.

And as for the t<u>a</u>st<u>e</u>, well what can I s<u>ay</u>?

It's str<u>a</u>nge—but I'll eat it all up anyw<u>ay</u>."

What Do We Mean by Phonics?

"Phonics" is the name we give to the association between particular letter patterns in words and the sounds they represent. By drawing children's attention to these symbol-sound relationships, we provide them with tools to help them sound out, or decode, words they have not seen before. Phonics is not the only approach to teaching reading, but it has proven to be helpful in the early stages of learning to read.

How Can This Book Help?

Each book in the *First Phonics Fun* series has been designed to focus on a particular group of sounds and their related letter patterns. The rhymes in this book feature three long vowel sounds:

long *i* as in s<u>igh</u>, r<u>i</u>de, tr<u>y</u>
long *u* as in g<u>r</u>ew, r<u>oo</u>m, f<u>u</u>me
long *a* as in w<u>ai</u>t, pl<u>a</u>te, s<u>ay</u>

You will find the featured vowel sound used repeatedly in the words that make up a particular rhyme. The vowels used to make those sounds are underlined in each instance. As you read the rhymes with your child, you will be helping him or her make the important connection between particular letters and their sounds.

How Should I Use This Book?

Children learn best when the experience is enjoyable. Read the rhymes to your child, and point out the sounds that are underlined. Then, help your child read through each rhyme with you. Finally, have your child try to read the stories by him- or herself.

Titles in the series: